WATER RAT'S
PICNIC

WATER RAT'S PICNIC

By Alison Uttley
Pictures by Margaret Tempest

templar publishing

ONE DAY WATER RAT came out of his house by the riverside. The garden was full of riverbank flowers, bright blue forget-me-nots, yellow flags and water-mint.

Water Rat whistled a sea-shanty and went towards his boathouse. There lay the *Saucy Nancy*, the neatest, prettiest little boat you ever saw! She had a pair of slender oars like scarlet wings. A couple of cushions lay on the seat, and a water jar was in the bow. Water Rat was very proud of his boat.

On this particular fine day Water Rat had packed a picnic basket.

"Where might you be going today, Sir?" asked Mrs Webster, his housekeeper.

"I'm going to invite some young friends of mine on a water-picnic," said Water Rat happily. "They've never seen a boat, I believe."

Water Rat settled himself in the boat and paddled peacefully upstream. Green dragonflies darted here and there, and a kingfisher shot by like a blue arrow. At the water's edge a brown water hen was busy with a heap of washing.

"A good drying day," said Water Rat, and the water hen looked up from her work.

"The ducks are very tiresome," she complained. "They tease me and carry off the washing."

"Never mind, you've got a fine young family to help you," said Water Rat.

A crowd of fluffy water chicks danced on the ripples. "Fourteen children," said the water hen proudly, "and every one of them is a champion swimmer."

Water Rat took up the oars and rowed some distance. He moored the boat to the roots of a willow and leapt out. Then he walked across the fields to Grey Rabbit's house.

He tapped at the door.

"Come in! Come in!" called Grey Rabbit, who was busy making strawberry jam.

"Oh, Water Rat! How pleased I am to see you!" she cried. "Do sit down. I shan't be long now. The strawberries are bubbling."

"Nice smell," said Water Rat, sinking into the rocking-chair and wiping his forehead. "We have no strawberries by the river."

"What kind of jam do you make?" asked Grey Rabbit.

"Lily-bud jam," said Water Rat.

Grey Rabbit ladled the jam into a row of little glass jars, and covered each with a strawberry leaf.

"I came to invite you and Squirrel to go for a picnic," said Water Rat. "My boat is moored by the old willow and the food is aboard."

"A picnic! A boat!" cried Little Grey Rabbit.

"A boat? A real live boat?" called Squirrel, dancing in on tiptoes.

"A picnic? A real live picnic?" shouted Hare, popping his head in at the window.

"I'm afraid my boat will only hold three," said Water Rat coldly.

Hare came into the room and stood in front of Water Rat.

"Look here," he cried. "Do you mean to say you are going on a picnic without me? It's impossible! What is there to eat, Water Rat?"

"Egg and cress sandwiches, marigold sponge, watermint jellies—"

"Stop! Stop!" moaned Hare.

"I'm afraid we can't go, Water Rat. We can't leave Hare behind," said Squirrel.

"I have a plan," said Water Rat. "Suppose you race along the river bank, Hare, while I row Grey Rabbit and Squirrel. Then you can choose the place for the picnic and we will all have a feast under the trees."

"That's a good idea!" said Hare. "It isn't the boat I want, but the picnic."

"That's settled then." Water Rat breathed again.

They shut their windows and locked the door, and put the key under the mat. Grey Rabbit carried a pot of strawberry jam, Hare his fishing net and Squirrel a pretty little sunshade. They tripped along by Water Rat's side, asking about the boat.

"Oh! how beautiful!" cried Grey Rabbit, when she saw the *Saucy Nancy* under the willow branches.

"You shall steer, Grey Rabbit," said Water Rat, "and Squirrel shall sit on a cushion."

He helped them both into the boat and untied the rope.

"Look at the waves, and the darting fishes, and the green weeds!" cried Grey Rabbit. She jumped with excitement as she saw the water so near.

Squirrel twirled her new sunshade, and glanced at her reflection in the clear river.

"Goodbye. Goodbye," called Hare. "I shall meet you soon. Take care of the food and don't fall in the river."

He galloped along the bank and they waved their paws to him. Soon he was out of sight.

Water Rat rowed with light, graceful sweeps of the scarlet oars. They saw a green frog sitting among the water-buttercups with a little fishing rod and a woven bag to hold his catch.

They stopped to chat with the water hen, and admired the fourteen little chicks which swam squeaking round the boat.

The little water hens scrambled along the oars and climbed on Grey Rabbit's knee, poking their beaks in her apron pocket.

"Come away, you naughty children," scolded their mother.

Grey Rabbit stroked their tiny brown heads before she lifted them back into the water.

There was a scurry and flurry, and a loud quacking as a flock of white ducks came hurrying up. The ducks swam up to the boat, diving and pushing.

"Where are you landlubbers going?" they asked.

"For a picnic," said Water Rat. "Don't come too near! You shake my boat."

One duck snatched Squirrel's sunshade and carried it off, laughing. Another pulled the strings of Grey Rabbit's little blue apron and swam away with it on her shoulders. Another twitched the ribbon from Squirrel's tail and a fourth seized the pot of strawberry jam.

There was such a commotion, such a rocking of the boat and a splash of water that nobody noticed another duck seize the picnic basket.

"Oh! Oh!" cried Grey Rabbit and Squirrel.

"It is outrageous!" said Water Rat.
He stared at one of the ducks. "Is it possible?
Has she taken the picnic basket?"

The duck held the little basket, and tried to
open it. As she struggled, the basket slipped and
went down, down to the bottom of the river.

"I'll get it," muttered Water Rat. He
took off his velvet coat and dived overboard.
Down to the bed of the river he went, and
among the waterweeds he found the basket.
He put his arms round it and swam back
to the boat. He hauled it over the side and
clambered after it. Then he rowed as fast as
he could, away from the ducks.

"Luckily it's lined with mackintosh," said Water Rat. "It won't be any the worse. But I'm sorry about your apron, Grey Rabbit, and your sunshade, Squirrel."

"I will make another apron," said Grey Rabbit, cheerfully.

"And I will have one of those big round leaves for a sunshade if you will pick it for me, Water Rat," said Squirrel.

Water Rat picked the lily leaf and Squirrel held it over her head and tried to forget her sunshade.

"Where's Hare?" asked Water Rat, staring at the river bank. "He ought to be waiting for us."

"Coo-oo," called Grey Rabbit. "Coo-oo, Hare."

"Coo-oo," came a faint reply.

Water Rat pulled the boat to the shore. From out of the reeds peered Hare, his coat torn and his net broken.

"Oh dear!" he cried. "I've been chased by a dog and tossed by a bull and bitten by gnats. And you've been rowing peacefully on the river."

"Not so peacefully," laughed Grey Rabbit. "I've lost my blue apron, Hare."

"And I've lost my sunshade," added Squirrel, leaping lightly out of the boat.

"And we nearly lost the picnic basket," said Water Rat.

"That would have been a calamity," muttered Hare. "A cal-cal-calamity!" He took the basket from Water Rat and clasped it to his heart.

Grey Rabbit and Squirrel ran about picking up sticks, and Water Rat carried the kettle and water jar to the hollow by the trees.

"Make a big fire!" called Hare. Water Rat struck a light. The fire crackled and yellow flames shot up. Squirrel balanced the kettle on top.

"Come along, Hare. You have more breath than any of us," said Squirrel.

Hare puffed out his cheeks and blew like the wind. Soon the kettle began to sing in its high shrill voice.

Water Rat unfastened the picnic basket.

Hare leapt for joy when he saw the patties and sandwiches and jellies in their waterproof wrappers. What a feast there was!

They laughed and sang and told their adventures, and quite forgot their troubles.

Hare was very hungry, for, he explained, he had run for miles, while they had been resting in the boat. "I was tossed by a gnat and bitten by a bull," said he, as he took the last sandwich.

"Bitten by a bulrush, you mean," said Water Rat.

They took the cups to the river edge and washed them and dried them on the grasses. They repacked the basket, then they sat down among the daisies to watch the river whirling below them.

Hare crept softly out of sight, and climbed into the boat. He untied the rope and pushed her into the stream.

"You didn't know I could row," he called, splashing with the scarlet oars. "It's quite easy."

"Oh Hare! Take care!" shrieked Squirrel, as the boat rocked dangerously.

"Sit down, Hare," said Water Rat. "You'll upset her if you stand up."

"Your boat is so wobbly," said Hare, swaying to one side. "Steady on there! Steady!"

Hare sat down with a thump, and the boat shook. He dipped the oars deep in the river and dragged up some weeds. Then the oars waved wildly, Hare's feet flew up, and he shot backwards into the water.

"Save me! Save me! I'm drowning!" he cried, kicking and struggling.

Out of the shadows came the ducks, one with the blue apron on her shoulders, another with the red sunshade above her head.

They circled round Hare and grabbed him by his fur. One took his left ear and another his right, another his leg and the fourth his coat tail. Then they swam to the shore with him.

They pushed him on the bank and away they went, cackling with laughter.

Squirrel and Grey Rabbit dried him with their handkerchiefs and squeezed the water out of his fur. The poor bedraggled Hare crouched over the fire, shivering.

"It's very wet in the river," he said. "I never knew that boat wasn't safe."

"You will have to run all the way home," said Grey Rabbit. "It will keep you from catching cold."

Water Rat swam after the little boat and the pair of oars which were floating down the river. He rowed back, dried the boat and wiped the cushions.

"I'm going home!" said Hare crossly. "I feel a chill in my bones." He started off along the river bank, trotting with head bent.

The others seated themselves in the boat, but Water Rat turned to Grey Rabbit.

"Would you like to see my house?" he asked. "It is quite near. There's watercress in my stream and I'll give you some to take home."

Grey Rabbit and Squirrel were delighted, and Water Rat turned the boat up the stream and stopped at the boathouse at the bottom of the garden. They walked up the garden path and entered the damp little house.

On a table in the hall stood an aquarium with duckweed and stickleback and minnows.

"Chirrup! Chirrup!" whistled Water Rat, and the tiny fish came swimming to the side of the tank and held up their noses.

Squirrel could hardly tear herself away
from this watery scene, but Water Rat led
the way to the parlour. It was very wet, and
Squirrel tucked her feet high as she sat on the
bulrush chair.

"Mrs Webster, will you bring some of your water-lily jam for my guests?" asked Water Rat.

Grey Rabbit and Squirrel smiled at the stout old water rat, and Mrs Webster fetched the little pots of lily jam and packed them in a bag for Grey Rabbit to carry.

"I'll get the watercress," said Water Rat.

"Oh, Miss Grey Rabbit and Miss Squirrel!" said Mrs Webster. "I am glad to see you! And how is Mister Hare? I suppose he couldn't go to the picnic, being too big for the boat?"

"Oh dear!" cried Grey Rabbit. "I'd forgotten about him! He fell in the river, Mrs Webster. We must hurry home."

"Hum! Always doing something, Mister Hare. Played noughts and crosses with the Fox, didn't he?" Mrs Webster smoothed her apron placidly.

Water Rat came paddling back with a basket of green cresses.

"We must go home," said Grey Rabbit, as she thanked him. "Poor Hare is waiting for us, all wet."

"Goodbye, Mrs Webster. Goodbye," they called, as they hurried away.

Water Rat rowed swiftly, and soon they were back at the old willow tree.

"Thank you, dear Water Rat. Thank you," they said, and they scampered home.

"Hare! Hare!" they called as they went into the house. "Guess what we did! We went to Water Rat's house and we saw... Hare, where are you?"

A violent sneeze shook the house. They ran upstairs to Hare's bedroom.

"A-tishoo!" sneezed Hare. "I thought you were both drowned! A-tishoo!"

Squirrel and Grey Rabbit raced round with herbs and hot water and soon Hare was snug in bed with a teapot of elderflower tea.

"Now, tell me all about it," said he.

So Little Grey Rabbit began to tell of Mrs Webster and the aquarium. Her silvery little voice went on with her tale, but Hare shut his eyes.

He was lulled by the sound, and before she had finished he was fast asleep. She tiptoed downstairs and joined Squirrel who was resting by the fire.

Pit-pat! Pit-pat! Little footsteps came flipping to the door. Then there was muffled laughter, and a shuffle and flop.

Grey Rabbit looked at Squirrel, and Squirrel looked at Grey Rabbit. Then, Pit-pat! Pitter-pat! Little footsteps went flipping down the garden path, flip-flopping over the grass. Quack! Quack!

Little Grey Rabbit stepped softly to the door and opened it. On the doorstep lay her blue apron, rather torn and dirty, and very wet.

"Oh, how glad I am to get my little apron again," she cried, and she hung it by the fire to dry.

But the sunshade never came back. The ducks liked it so much they wouldn't part with it. Any day you could see them swimming down the river, one of them carrying Squirrel's sunshade, and another playing with her ribbon bow.

WHICH LITTLE GREY RABBIT BOOKS DO YOU HAVE?

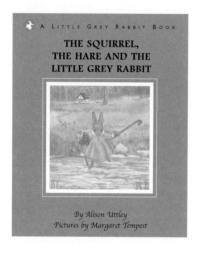

LITTLE GREY RABBIT'S VALENTINE

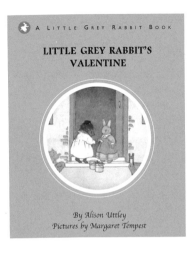

By Alison Uttley
Pictures by Margaret Tempest

HARE AND THE EASTER EGGS

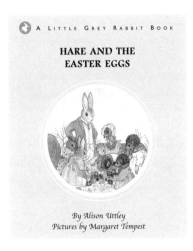

By Alison Uttley
Pictures by Margaret Tempest

LITTLE GREY RABBIT'S BIRTHDAY

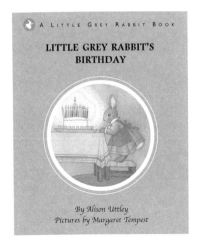

By Alison Uttley
Pictures by Margaret Tempest

THE STORY OF FUZZYPEG THE HEDGEHOG

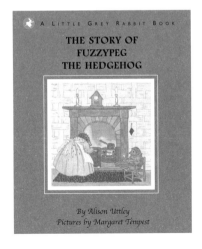

By Alison Uttley
Pictures by Margaret Tempest

A TEMPLAR BOOK

This edition first published in the UK in 2016 by Templar Publishing,
part of the Bonnier Publishing Group,
The Plaza, 535 King's Road, London, SW10 0SZ
www.templarco.co.uk
www.bonnierpublishing.com

Original edition first published in the UK in 1943
by William Collins Sons & Co Ltd

This edition edited by Susan Dickinson and Katie Haworth
Additional design by Kieran Hood

1 3 5 7 9 10 8 6 4 2

ISBN 978-1-78370-406-4

Printed in China